CONNECTED

A Personal Journal for Ketamine Therapy

Katherine Inez Davis

This journal was created from research specific to clinical ketamine therapy, and it is intended for patients in a medically supervised treatment program. This journal can support, but not replace, associated work with a professional counselor or medical team.

All use is at the discretion of the individual.

Printed in the United States of America
Published in Hellertown, PA
Design by Dina Hall Graphic Design
Library of Congress Control Number: 2022921134
ISBN 978-1-958711-25-5
2 4 6 8 10 9 7 5 3 1

For more information or to place bulk orders, contact the author or Jennifer@BrightCommunications.net.

CONNECTED

A Personal Journal for Ketamine Therapy

introduction

Dear Friend,

I believe:

- You are a thoughtful, bright, positive person.
- You are weighed down or feel ruled by long-standing mental, emotional, and physical challenges that are very real.
- You already tried traditional methods, such as medications, counseling, and alternative therapies to address this.
- You research and read everything you can find to improve your circumstance.
- You are still suffering.
- You are ready to open yourself to the unique option ketamine therapy offers.

When I sat in your spot, I was all of these. I still am. When I stumbled across ketamine therapy for treatment-resistant depression, I dove into research. The information I found about how ketamine works against and through depression, trauma, PTSD, chronic pain, and related conditions mesmerized me.

If I had to summarize what stuck with me from my many "how does this stuff work..." late-night internet searches, I would try this: Ketamine, when administered under medical supervision carefully tailored to a patient, seems to silence painful ruminations, negative self thoughts, and traumatic reruns for a short time. Inside that mini mind-vacation, a rush of positive emotions can fill the space. In that moment, when a person suddenly knows kindness, joyful feelings, and a pain-free existence, ketamine opens an incredible window of relief, optimism, and healing.

My late-night searches also showed that patients can take active steps alongside their ketamine treatment for improved outcomes. It is like physical therapy after surgery: Other activities help this major medical treatment become more successful. One of these steps is journaling.

Ketamine therapy is not solely about the hour when the drug is active in your system. That is simply the starting point. How you move forward matters just as much. A journal is a useful accessory for the on-going integration phase of your ketamine treatment and is your chance to actively take control of your recovery.

When I started ketamine therapy, I prepared a blank, ring-bound journal and recorded thoughts and reactions before, immediately after, and in between treatment sessions. I could not guess that in four weeks, I would create a resource that allows me to call upon one of the most unexpected, comforting, and powerful experiences I have ever known. When I read those pages now, I know how much I would have forgotten if I had not written it down. I recognize the importance of every detail I recorded.

A Formal Study: When I researched and then pursued ketamine therapy, I was nearing the end of a master's degree program in professional writing. The timing was no coincidence. With deep study into ketamine therapy in hand and completely impressed by my own journaling experience, I looked into joining these as a formal study to complete my graduate program. My thesis was accepted, and the pages ahead of you grew out of that work.

In this study, I collected public accounts from ketamine patients, broke down their stories, studied the language they used to express their experience with ketamine, and found strong, undeniably consistent themes. I was, in no small way, transfixed by looking carefully inside the patient experience and deeply affected by their candid personal stories. After more than a year of intrigue and academic work, I had the information and data needed to create a useable patient journal. Here it is!

A Focused Journal: That study showed three main topics ketamine patients discussed. The first is Prep: preparation for treatment by sharing and reviewing the condition that brought them to ketamine therapy and describing what life is like with that condition. Second is Recall: recalling the experience, sensations, and thoughts that occur during a treatment session. The third theme is Connection: thinking through the experience, noting changes to thought patterns, and applying these into life outcomes. Therefore, the journal is designed accordingly into these three: Prep Pages, Recall Pages, and Connection Pages. This journal was designed to fit these categories and work in partnership with your treatment. The ketamine will fade away. Your words, captured here, will remain available to revisit and explore.

My Wish for You: I don't know what lies ahead for you. I believe it may include wonderful highs, challenging lows, and great clarity to guide you forward. I invite you to use these pages to connect any gifts ketamine therapy offers you. No matter what scars mark your heart or cloud your mind, I believe there is space left to write a new story. Start here.

– Katee

using your journal

Ketamine treatment may be a tremendous, unusual experience. It is also a fast and heavy hour or more of sensory, emotional, and mental missives. The full scope of details within that experience can be hard to remember and explain. Using a journal with focused prompts helps to vividly capture your experience and hold on to any concepts, peace, or relief that was accessed.

Because your journal is your decision to improve the outcomes from your therapy, I recommend giving your journal – and yourself! – time and attention. You may wish to find a neutral or calm space to think and write. Clear ample time in your schedule to devote to this practice. Give yourself a pass on achieving "good writing." Proper grammar and flow are not the goals on these pages. Details and experiences are the priorities here.

The prompts of the journal are a result of specific data from my research study. However, they are crafted loosely enough to fit your distinctive experience. The prompts are not provided to influence your experience in the ketamine session. Instead, they are here to help find and record these memories. If you do not relate to a certain prompt, just skip to the parts that feel important for you.

The big picture of the exercise is to collect your experiences, continually review your previous thoughts, and, at your comfort, bring this to a professional counselor or trusted support group to sort through your notes. Together, you can find meaning and connection from your ketamine sessions to create a framework for action and improvement in your daily life.

section one **Prep Pages**

Prior to a treatment, these pages allow you to assess your current energy, focus, and outlook levels. There is also space to consider how you currently measure a regular day, a great day, or a hard day.

- Write where you spend free time, if any, and your current outlets in hobbies, creative arts, or spiritual pursuits. In health and wellness, add in the activities you are already trying or would like to try, including meditation, time in nature, exercise, or nutritional changes.

- In what's happening, briefly note circumstances in major life areas that may be on your mind. This will serve as a reminder of changing situations as you look back in the months ahead.

- As you consider your next treatment, collect some of your emotions, hopes, and fears here. If you are forming an intention, you may consider what you are missing and would like to find and what anchors are holding you back that you would gladly lose to the ketamine.

- Noting your preparation is included to encourage you to spend time prior to treatment thoughtfully and purposely, and mark any differences in how your prep may affect treatment outcomes. All of this will translate into your mindset for the next pages and for your treatment. Did you read, rest, take time alone, or turn off your phone, email, and social media to clear your head before a treatment?

section two **Recall Pages**

It is best to complete treatment recall pages as soon after a session as possible or on the same day as treatment. These truly are to collect as much detail as you can.

The initial prompts will record your set and setting – chart your place, music, and the person or sitter who will be with you. Record your mindset – thoughts or intentions that were present before you were administered the ketamine.

- Now you are ready for recall. How did you know the ketamine had hit your system? What were the first indications of a change? Was it a feeling? A visual? A sense?

- In "what I saw," consider colors, visuals, shapes, movement.

- In "what I heard," consider voices, words, and messages.

- In "what I felt," try to express your body and sense of self. What words describe the emotions you felt? Was any emotion unfamiliar?

- Use the "where" line to describe any space or place that entered your mind.

- Finally, consider who was part of your experience, such as family or friends. Was it visually or through some kind of interaction? How can you describe that connection?

- Then, describe your transition out of the treatment. How did you first know the ketamine was wearing off? What did you feel as it left your system?

- There is also space for anything that is confusing or odd. Maybe it will make sense later, so it is important not to brush it off. Fuzzy areas may become clear in review with your counselor or support network.

- Did your sitter notice you speak, move, laugh, or express any emotion?

- Assess your feelings of self-worth and outlook as soon as you have completely recorded your notes from this session.

Continue to jot notes on these pages if you remember more in hours and days after treatment. Also start to write any of your interpretations and reactions to the treatment. Read your own words again as frequently as you wish to help connect those experiences, clarify any messages, and assist the process of integrating your treatment into recovery.

section three **Connection Pages**

Because clinical ketamine treatment is often administered in a generally accepted formula of six treatments in a set of weeks, the timing of the treatments creates ample room for journaling. Your journal is the bridge from one moment of healing to the next.

- In days after and between treatments, assess your focus, energy, and outlook. Reread your experience now that some time has passed. What does it feel like to read your words?

- Revisit the great day, hard day, and regular day levels. Are there improvements to your routine or declines from day to day?

- Insights: Has any part of your treatment memory had the most affect? What do these visuals and audio mean to you now? Did your intention guide this in any way?

- Ideas: What do you want to share with your counselor, guide, or support group? Consider perspective, emotions, and attitudes.

- Have you gained any motivation to start or increase hobbies, overall health steps, or new activities?

- In "what's happening" can you review your original circumstances? What is your view of these now? Can you apply a new perspective?

- Any Time Lines encourage you to write, write, write at any time in your treatment. How you continue to relive and consider your experience is an extension of your therapy and will continue to support growth and healing.

Six sets of pages are provided to carry you through a treatment series. Three extra sets of Connection Pages end the journal to support integration after ketamine therapy.

Your Ongoing Work

Bring your journal to your counselor as a powerful tool for discussion and analysis. This allows any helpful moments to extend past the treatment and gain a place naturally in your life. You may return to the journal, read the memories of your past experiences, and continue to develop coping mechanisms, new insights, and personal strength to move forward, better.

Prep Pages

Today's Date:_____

Next Treatment: _____

CURRENT OR RECENT STATUS

Energy Level: 1 2 3 4 5 6 7 8 9 10

Focus Level: 1 2 3 4 5 6 7 8 9 10

Overall Outlook: 1 2 3 4 5 6 7 8 9 10

A regular day looks like: _____

_____

_____

A great day looks like: _____

_____

_____

A hard day looks like: _____

_____

_____

_____

OUTLETS

Hobbies:_____

_____

Spiritual: _____

_____

Creative: _____

_____

Health and wellness: _____

_____

WHAT'S HAPPENING

At home: _____

_____

_____

At work: _____

_____

_____

With family: _____

_____

_____

With friends: _____

_____

_____

Personal goals: _____

_____

_____

OUTLOOK FOR TREATMENT

Emotions: _____

_____

_____

Hopes: _____

_____

_____

Fears: _____

_____

_____

I'd like to find:

_____

_____

I'd like to leave behind:

_____

_____

PREPARATION

I prepared for this treatment by:

_____

_____

_____

_____

_____

OTHER NOTES

_____

_____

_____

_____

_____

_____

_____

_____

_____

Recall Pages

SET AND SETTING

Intention and thoughts immediately before treatment:

_____

_____

_____

Dose: _____   Sitter: _____

Place: _____   Music: _____

ENTRY

First sensations in treatment: _____

_____

_____

_____

_____

_____

What I saw: _____

_____

_____

_____

What I heard: _____

_____

What I felt, physically: _____

_____

_____

Emotionally: _____

_____

_____

Spiritually: _____

_____

_____

Where I was: _____

_____

_____

Who I remember: _____

_____

_____

EXIT

Thoughts coming out of treatment: _____

_____

_____

Emotions coming out of treatment: _____

_____

_____

REACTIONS

Was any part of the treatment exceptional? _____

_____

_____

Was any part of the treatment unpleasant? _____

_____

_____

Experiences in treatment to consider later: _____

_____

_____

Observations from sitter: _____

_____

_____

_____

_____

Other thoughts from treatment: _____

_____

_____

_____

_____

Right at this moment, my feelings about myself are: 1 2 3 4 5 6 7 8 9 10

OTHER NOTES

Additional memories after treatment: _____

Connection Pages

Today's Date: _____

CURRENT OR RECENT STATUS

Energy Level: 1 2 3 4 5 6 7 8 9 10

Focus Level: 1 2 3 4 5 6 7 8 9 10

Overall Outlook: 1 2 3 4 5 6 7 8 9 10

LOOKING BACK

When I read my notes from the treatment session, I feel: _____

_____

_____

_____

I notice these improvements, if any: _____

_____

_____

_____

I feel discouraged in these ways, if any: _____

_____

_____

_____

Insights since treatment: _____

_____

_____

_____

MOVING FORWARD

Ideas to review with counselor or guide: _____

_____

_____

_____

_____

_____

_____

_____

_____

_____

NEW OR UPDATED OUTLETS

Hobbies: _____

_____

_____

Spiritual: _____

_____

_____

Creative: _____

_____

_____

Health and wellness: _____

_____

_____

HOW I FEEL ABOUT WHAT'S HAPPENING

At home: _____

_____

_____

At work: _____

_____

_____

With family: _____

_____

_____

With friends: _____

_____

_____

Personal goals: _____

_____

_____

_____

_____

_____

_____

_____

Any Time Lines

Prep Pages

Today's Date:_____

Next Treatment: _____

CURRENT OR RECENT STATUS

Energy Level: 1 2 3 4 5 6 7 8 9 10

Focus Level: 1 2 3 4 5 6 7 8 9 10

Overall Outlook: 1 2 3 4 5 6 7 8 9 10

A regular day looks like: _____

_____

_____

A great day looks like: _____

_____

_____

A hard day looks like: _____

_____

_____

_____

OUTLETS

Hobbies:_____

_____

Spiritual: _____

_____

Creative: _____

_____

Health and wellness: _____

_____

WHAT'S HAPPENING

At home: _____

_____

_____

At work: _____

_____

_____

With family: _____

_____

_____

With friends: _____

_____

_____

Personal goals: _____

_____

_____

OUTLOOK FOR TREATMENT

Emotions: _____

_____

_____

Hopes: _____

_____

_____

Fears: _____

_____

_____

I'd like to find:

I'd like to leave behind:

PREPARATION

I prepared for this treatment by:

OTHER NOTES

Recall Pages

SET AND SETTING

Intention and thoughts immediately before treatment:

_____

_____

_____

Dose: _____   Sitter: _____

Place: _____   Music: _____

ENTRY

First sensations in treatment: _____

_____

_____

_____

_____

_____

What I saw: _____

_____

_____

_____

What I heard: _____

_____

_____

What I felt, physically: _____

_____

_____

Emotionally: _____

_____

_____

Spiritually: _____

_____

_____

Where I was: _____

_____

_____

Who I remember: _____

_____

_____

EXIT

Thoughts coming out of treatment: _____

_____

_____

Emotions coming out of treatment: _____

_____

_____

REACTIONS

Was any part of the treatment exceptional? _____

_____

_____

Was any part of the treatment unpleasant? _____

_____

_____

Experiences in treatment to consider later: _____

_____

_____

Observations from sitter: _____

_____

_____

_____

_____

Other thoughts from treatment: _____

_____

_____

_____

_____

Right at this moment, my feelings about myself are: 1 2 3 4 5 6 7 8 9 10

OTHER NOTES

Additional memories after treatment: _____

_____

_____

_____

_____

_____

_____

_____

_____

_____

_____

_____

_____

_____

_____

_____

_____

_____

_____

_____

_____

_____

_____

_____

Connection Pages

Today's Date: _____

CURRENT OR RECENT STATUS

Energy Level: 1 2 3 4 5 6 7 8 9 10

Focus Level: 1 2 3 4 5 6 7 8 9 10

Overall Outlook: 1 2 3 4 5 6 7 8 9 10

LOOKING BACK

When I read my notes from the treatment session, I feel: _____

_____

_____

_____

I notice these improvements, if any: _____

_____

_____

_____

I feel discouraged in these ways, if any: _____

_____

_____

_____

Insights since treatment: _____

_____

_____

_____

MOVING FORWARD

Ideas to review with counselor or guide: _____

_____

_____

_____

_____

_____

_____

_____

NEW OR UPDATED OUTLETS

Hobbies: _____

_____

_____

Spiritual: _____

_____

_____

Creative: _____

_____

_____

Health and wellness: _____

_____

_____

HOW I FEEL ABOUT WHAT'S HAPPENING

At home: _____

_____

_____

_____

At work: _____

_____

_____

_____

With family: _____

_____

_____

_____

With friends: _____

_____

_____

_____

Personal goals: _____

_____

_____

_____

_____

_____

_____

_____

Any Time Lines

Prep Pages

Today's Date:_____

Next Treatment:_____

CURRENT OR RECENT STATUS

Energy Level: 1 2 3 4 5 6 7 8 9 10

Focus Level: 1 2 3 4 5 6 7 8 9 10

Overall Outlook: 1 2 3 4 5 6 7 8 9 10

A regular day looks like:_____

_____

_____

A great day looks like:_____

_____

_____

A hard day looks like:_____

_____

_____

_____

OUTLETS

Hobbies:_____

_____

Spiritual:_____

_____

Creative:_____

_____

Health and wellness:_____

_____

WHAT'S HAPPENING

At home: _____

_____

_____

At work: _____

_____

_____

With family: _____

_____

_____

With friends: _____

_____

_____

Personal goals: _____

_____

_____

OUTLOOK FOR TREATMENT

Emotions: _____

_____

_____

Hopes: _____

_____

_____

Fears: _____

_____

_____

I'd like to find: _____

_____

_____

I'd like to leave behind: _____

_____

_____

PREPARATION

I prepared for this treatment by: _____

_____

_____

_____

_____

_____

OTHER NOTES

_____

_____

_____

_____

_____

_____

_____

_____

_____

_____

_____

Recall Pages

SET AND SETTING

Intention and thoughts immediately before treatment:

_____

_____

_____

Dose: _____   Sitter: _____

Place: _____   Music: _____

ENTRY

First sensations in treatment: _____

_____

_____

_____

_____

_____

What I saw: _____

_____

_____

_____

What I heard: _____

_____

_____

What I felt, physically: _____

_____

_____

Emotionally: _____

_____

_____

Spiritually: _____

_____

_____

_____

Where I was: _____

_____

_____

_____

Who I remember: _____

_____

_____

_____

EXIT

Thoughts coming out of treatment: _____

_____

_____

_____

Emotions coming out of treatment: _____

_____

_____

REACTIONS

Was any part of the treatment exceptional? _____

_____

_____

Was any part of the treatment unpleasant? _____

_____

_____

Experiences in treatment to consider later: _____

_____

_____

Observations from sitter: _____

_____

_____

_____

_____

Other thoughts from treatment: _____

_____

_____

_____

_____

Right at this moment, my feelings about myself are: 1 2 3 4 5 6 7 8 9 10

OTHER NOTES

Additional memories after treatment: _____

_____

_____

_____

_____

_____

_____

_____

_____

_____

_____

_____

_____

_____

_____

_____

_____

_____

_____

_____

_____

_____

_____

_____

_____

Connection Pages

Today's Date: _____

CURRENT OR RECENT STATUS

Energy Level: 1 2 3 4 5 6 7 8 9 10

Focus Level: 1 2 3 4 5 6 7 8 9 10

Overall Outlook: 1 2 3 4 5 6 7 8 9 10

LOOKING BACK

When I read my notes from the treatment session, I feel: _____

_____

_____

_____

I notice these improvements, if any: _____

_____

_____

_____

I feel discouraged in these ways, if any: _____

_____

_____

_____

Insights since treatment: _____

_____

_____

_____

MOVING FORWARD

Ideas to review with counselor or guide: _____

_____

_____

_____

_____

_____

_____

_____

_____

NEW OR UPDATED OUTLETS

Hobbies: _____

_____

_____

Spiritual: _____

_____

_____

Creative: _____

_____

_____

Health and wellness: _____

_____

_____

_____

HOW I FEEL ABOUT WHAT'S HAPPENING

At home: _____

_____

_____

At work: _____

_____

_____

With family: _____

_____

_____

With friends: _____

_____

_____

Personal goals: _____

_____

_____

_____

_____

_____

_____

_____

_____

Any Time Lines

Today's Date: _____

Prep Pages

Today's Date:_____

Next Treatment: _____

CURRENT OR RECENT STATUS

Energy Level: 1 2 3 4 5 6 7 8 9 10

Focus Level: 1 2 3 4 5 6 7 8 9 10

Overall Outlook: 1 2 3 4 5 6 7 8 9 10

A regular day looks like: _____

_____

_____

A great day looks like: _____

_____

_____

A hard day looks like: _____

_____

_____

_____

OUTLETS

Hobbies:_____

_____

Spiritual: _____

_____

Creative: _____

_____

Health and wellness: _____

_____

WHAT'S HAPPENING

At home: _____

_____

_____

At work: _____

_____

_____

With family: _____

_____

_____

With friends: _____

_____

_____

Personal goals: _____

_____

_____

OUTLOOK FOR TREATMENT

Emotions: _____

_____

_____

Hopes: _____

_____

_____

Fears: _____

_____

_____

I'd like to find:

I'd like to leave behind:

PREPARATION

I prepared for this treatment by:

OTHER NOTES

Recall Pages

Treatment Date: _____

SET AND SETTING

Intention and thoughts immediately before treatment:

_____

_____

_____

Dose: _____   Sitter: _____

Place: _____   Music: _____

ENTRY

First sensations in treatment: _____

_____

_____

_____

_____

_____

What I saw: _____

_____

_____

_____

What I heard: _____

_____

_____

What I felt, physically: _____

_____

_____

Emotionally: _____

_____

_____

Spiritually: _____

_____

_____

Where I was: _____

_____

_____

Who I remember: _____

_____

_____

EXIT

Thoughts coming out of treatment: _____

_____

_____

Emotions coming out of treatment: _____

_____

_____

REACTIONS

Was any part of the treatment exceptional? _____

_____

_____

Was any part of the treatment unpleasant? _____

_____

_____

Experiences in treatment to consider later: _____

_____

_____

Observations from sitter: _____

_____

_____

_____

_____

Other thoughts from treatment: _____

_____

_____

_____

_____

Right at this moment, my feelings about myself are: 1 2 3 4 5 6 7 8 9 10

OTHER NOTES

Additional memories after treatment: _____

_____

_____

_____

_____

_____

_____

_____

_____

_____

_____

_____

_____

_____

_____

_____

_____

_____

_____

_____

_____

_____

_____

_____

_____

Connection Pages

Today's Date: _____

CURRENT OR RECENT STATUS

Energy Level: 1 2 3 4 5 6 7 8 9 10

Focus Level: 1 2 3 4 5 6 7 8 9 10

Overall Outlook: 1 2 3 4 5 6 7 8 9 10

LOOKING BACK

When I read my notes from the treatment session, I feel: _____

_____

_____

_____

I notice these improvements, if any: _____

_____

_____

_____

I feel discouraged in these ways, if any:_____

_____

_____

_____

Insights since treatment: _____

_____

_____

_____

MOVING FORWARD

Ideas to review with counselor or guide: _____

_____

_____

_____

_____

_____

_____

_____

_____

NEW OR UPDATED OUTLETS

Hobbies: _____

_____

_____

Spiritual: _____

_____

_____

Creative: _____

_____

_____

Health and wellness: _____

_____

_____

HOW I FEEL ABOUT WHAT'S HAPPENING

At home: _____

_____

_____

_____

At work: _____

_____

_____

_____

With family: _____

_____

_____

_____

With friends: _____

_____

_____

_____

Personal goals: _____

_____

_____

_____

_____

_____

_____

_____

_____

_____

Any Time Lines

Prep Pages

Today's Date:_____

Next Treatment: _____

CURRENT OR RECENT STATUS

Energy Level: 1 2 3 4 5 6 7 8 9 10

Focus Level: 1 2 3 4 5 6 7 8 9 10

Overall Outlook: 1 2 3 4 5 6 7 8 9 10

A regular day looks like: _____

_____

_____

A great day looks like: _____

_____

_____

A hard day looks like: _____

_____

_____

_____

OUTLETS

Hobbies:_____

_____

Spiritual: _____

_____

Creative: _____

_____

Health and wellness: _____

_____

WHAT'S HAPPENING

At home: _____

_____

_____

At work: _____

_____

_____

With family: _____

_____

_____

With friends: _____

_____

_____

Personal goals: _____

_____

_____

OUTLOOK FOR TREATMENT

Emotions: _____

_____

_____

Hopes: _____

_____

_____

Fears: _____

_____

_____

I'd like to find:

I'd like to leave behind:

PREPARATION

I prepared for this treatment by:

OTHER NOTES

Recall Pages

SET AND SETTING

Intention and thoughts immediately before treatment:

_____

_____

_____

Dose: _____   Sitter: _____

Place: _____   Music: _____

ENTRY

First sensations in treatment: _____

_____

_____

_____

_____

_____

What I saw: _____

_____

_____

_____

What I heard: _____

_____

_____

What I felt, physically: _____

_____

_____

Emotionally: _____

_____

_____

Spiritually: _____

_____

_____

Where I was: _____

_____

_____

Who I remember: _____

_____

_____

EXIT

Thoughts coming out of treatment: _____

_____

_____

Emotions coming out of treatment: _____

_____

_____

REACTIONS

Was any part of the treatment exceptional? _____

_____

_____

Was any part of the treatment unpleasant? _____

_____

_____

Experiences in treatment to consider later: _____

_____

_____

Observations from sitter: _____

_____

_____

_____

_____

Other thoughts from treatment: _____

_____

_____

_____

_____

Right at this moment, my feelings about myself are: 1 2 3 4 5 6 7 8 9 10

OTHER NOTES

Additional memories after treatment: _____

_____

_____

_____

_____

_____

_____

_____

_____

_____

_____

_____

_____

_____

_____

_____

_____

_____

_____

_____

_____

_____

_____

_____

Connection Pages

Today's Date: _____

CURRENT OR RECENT STATUS

Energy Level: 1 2 3 4 5 6 7 8 9 10

Focus Level: 1 2 3 4 5 6 7 8 9 10

Overall Outlook: 1 2 3 4 5 6 7 8 9 10

LOOKING BACK

When I read my notes from the treatment session, I feel: _____

_____

_____

_____

I notice these improvements, if any: _____

_____

_____

_____

I feel discouraged in these ways, if any: _____

_____

_____

_____

Insights since treatment: _____

_____

_____

_____

MOVING FORWARD

Ideas to review with counselor or guide: _____

_____

_____

_____

_____

_____

_____

_____

_____

_____

_____

NEW OR UPDATED OUTLETS

Hobbies: _____

_____

_____

Spiritual: _____

_____

_____

Creative: _____

_____

_____

Health and wellness: _____

_____

_____

HOW I FEEL ABOUT WHAT'S HAPPENING

At home: _____

_____

_____

_____

At work: _____

_____

_____

_____

With family: _____

_____

_____

_____

With friends: _____

_____

_____

_____

Personal goals: _____

_____

_____

_____

_____

_____

_____

_____

_____

_____

Any Time Lines

Today's Date: _____

Prep Pages

Today's Date:_____

Next Treatment: _____

CURRENT OR RECENT STATUS

Energy Level: 1 2 3 4 5 6 7 8 9 10

Focus Level: 1 2 3 4 5 6 7 8 9 10

Overall Outlook: 1 2 3 4 5 6 7 8 9 10

A regular day looks like: _____
_____
_____

A great day looks like: _____
_____
_____

A hard day looks like: _____
_____
_____
_____

OUTLETS

Hobbies:_____
_____

Spiritual: _____
_____

Creative: _____
_____

Health and wellness: _____
_____

WHAT'S HAPPENING

At home: _____

_____

_____

At work: _____

_____

_____

With family: _____

_____

_____

With friends: _____

_____

_____

Personal goals: _____

_____

_____

OUTLOOK FOR TREATMENT

Emotions: _____

_____

_____

Hopes: _____

_____

_____

Fears: _____

_____

_____

I'd like to find:

I'd like to leave behind:

PREPARATION

I prepared for this treatment by:

OTHER NOTES

Recall Pages

SET AND SETTING

Intention and thoughts immediately before treatment:

_____

_____

_____

Dose: _____   Sitter: _____

Place: _____   Music: _____

ENTRY

First sensations in treatment: _____

_____

_____

_____

_____

_____

What I saw: _____

_____

_____

_____

What I heard: _____

_____

_____

What I felt, physically: _____

_____

_____

Emotionally: _____

_____

_____

Spiritually: _____

_____

_____

_____

Where I was: _____

_____

_____

_____

Who I remember: _____

_____

_____

EXIT

Thoughts coming out of treatment: _____

_____

_____

Emotions coming out of treatment: _____

_____

_____

REACTIONS

Was any part of the treatment exceptional? _____

_____

_____

Was any part of the treatment unpleasant? _____

_____

_____

Experiences in treatment to consider later: _____

_____

_____

Observations from sitter: _____

_____

_____

_____

_____

Other thoughts from treatment: _____

_____

_____

_____

_____

Right at this moment, my feelings about myself are: 1 2 3 4 5 6 7 8 9 10

OTHER NOTES

Additional memories after treatment: _____

_____

_____

_____

_____

_____

_____

_____

_____

_____

_____

_____

_____

_____

_____

_____

_____

_____

_____

_____

_____

_____

_____

Connection Pages  Today's Date: _____

CURRENT OR RECENT STATUS

Energy Level: 1 2 3 4 5 6 7 8 9 10

Focus Level: 1 2 3 4 5 6 7 8 9 10

Overall Outlook: 1 2 3 4 5 6 7 8 9 10

LOOKING BACK

When I read my notes from the treatment session, I feel: _____

_____

_____

_____

I notice these improvements, if any: _____

_____

_____

_____

I feel discouraged in these ways, if any: _____

_____

_____

_____

Insights since treatment: _____

_____

_____

_____

MOVING FORWARD

Ideas to review with counselor or guide: _____

_____

_____

_____

_____

_____

_____

_____

_____

NEW OR UPDATED OUTLETS

Hobbies:_____

_____

_____

Spiritual:_____

_____

_____

Creative:_____

_____

_____

Health and wellness:_____

_____

_____

_____

HOW I FEEL ABOUT WHAT'S HAPPENING

At home: _____

_____

_____

_____

At work: _____

_____

_____

With family: _____

_____

_____

_____

With friends: _____

_____

_____

_____

Personal goals: _____

_____

_____

_____

_____

_____

_____

_____

_____

_____

Any Time Lines

Today's Date: _____

Prep Pages

Today's Date:_____

Next Treatment: _____

CURRENT OR RECENT STATUS

Energy Level: 1 2 3 4 5 6 7 8 9 10

Focus Level: 1 2 3 4 5 6 7 8 9 10

Overall Outlook: 1 2 3 4 5 6 7 8 9 10

A regular day looks like:_____

_____

_____

A great day looks like:_____

_____

_____

A hard day looks like:_____

_____

_____

_____

OUTLETS

Hobbies:_____

_____

Spiritual:_____

_____

Creative:_____

_____

Health and wellness:_____

_____

WHAT'S HAPPENING

At home: _____

_____

_____

At work: _____

_____

_____

With family: _____

_____

_____

With friends: _____

_____

_____

Personal goals: _____

_____

_____

OUTLOOK FOR TREATMENT

Emotions: _____

_____

_____

Hopes: _____

_____

_____

Fears: _____

_____

_____

I'd like to find:

I'd like to leave behind:

PREPARATION

I prepared for this treatment by:

OTHER NOTES

Recall Pages

Treatment Date: _____

SET AND SETTING

Intention and thoughts immediately before treatment:

_____

_____

_____

Dose: _____   Sitter: _____

Place: _____   Music: _____

ENTRY

First sensations in treatment: _____

_____

_____

_____

_____

What I saw: _____

_____

_____

_____

What I heard: _____

_____

_____

What I felt, physically: _____

_____

_____

Emotionally: _____

_____

_____

Spiritually: _____

_____

_____

_____

Where I was: _____

_____

_____

_____

Who I remember: _____

_____

_____

_____

EXIT

Thoughts coming out of treatment: _____

_____

_____

_____

Emotions coming out of treatment: _____

_____

_____

_____

REACTIONS

Was any part of the treatment exceptional? _____

_____

_____

Was any part of the treatment unpleasant? _____

_____

_____

Experiences in treatment to consider later: _____

_____

_____

Observations from sitter: _____

_____

_____

_____

_____

Other thoughts from treatment: _____

_____

_____

_____

_____

Right at this moment, my feelings about myself are: 1 2 3 4 5 6 7 8 9 10

OTHER NOTES

Additional memories after treatment: _____

_____

_____

_____

_____

_____

_____

_____

_____

_____

_____

_____

_____

_____

_____

_____

_____

_____

_____

_____

_____

_____

_____

_____

_____

_____

_____

Connection Pages

Today's Date: _____

CURRENT OR RECENT STATUS

Energy Level: 1 2 3 4 5 6 7 8 9 10

Focus Level: 1 2 3 4 5 6 7 8 9 10

Overall Outlook: 1 2 3 4 5 6 7 8 9 10

LOOKING BACK

When I read my notes from the treatment session, I feel: _____

_____

_____

_____

I notice these improvements, if any: _____

_____

_____

_____

I feel discouraged in these ways, if any: _____

_____

_____

_____

Insights since treatment: _____

_____

_____

_____

MOVING FORWARD

Ideas to review with counselor or guide: _____

_____

_____

_____

_____

_____

_____

_____

_____

NEW OR UPDATED OUTLETS

Hobbies: _____

_____

_____

Spiritual: _____

_____

_____

Creative: _____

_____

_____

Health and wellness: _____

_____

_____

HOW I FEEL ABOUT WHAT'S HAPPENING

At home: _____

_____

_____

_____

At work: _____

_____

_____

_____

With family: _____

_____

_____

_____

With friends: _____

_____

_____

_____

Personal goals: _____

_____

_____

_____

_____

_____

_____

_____

_____

_____

Any Time Lines

Connection Pages

Today's Date: _____

CURRENT OR RECENT STATUS

Energy Level: 1 2 3 4 5 6 7 8 9 10

Focus Level: 1 2 3 4 5 6 7 8 9 10

Overall Outlook: 1 2 3 4 5 6 7 8 9 10

LOOKING BACK

When I read my notes from the treatment session, I feel: _____

_____

_____

_____

I notice these improvements, if any: _____

_____

_____

_____

I feel discouraged in these ways, if any: _____

_____

_____

_____

Insights since treatment: _____

_____

_____

_____

MOVING FORWARD

Ideas to review with counselor or guide: _____

_____

_____

_____

_____

_____

_____

_____

_____

_____

NEW OR UPDATED OUTLETS

Hobbies: _____

_____

_____

Spiritual: _____

_____

_____

Creative: _____

_____

_____

Health and wellness: _____

_____

_____

_____

HOW I FEEL ABOUT WHAT'S HAPPENING

At home: _____

_____

_____

_____

At work: _____

_____

_____

_____

With family: _____

_____

_____

_____

With friends: _____

_____

_____

_____

Personal goals: _____

_____

_____

_____

_____

_____

_____

_____

_____

_____

_____

Any Time Lines

Today's Date: _____

Connection Pages

Today's Date: _____

CURRENT OR RECENT STATUS

Energy Level: 1 2 3 4 5 6 7 8 9 10

Focus Level: 1 2 3 4 5 6 7 8 9 10

Overall Outlook: 1 2 3 4 5 6 7 8 9 10

LOOKING BACK

When I read my notes from the treatment session, I feel: _____

_____

_____

_____

I notice these improvements, if any: _____

_____

_____

_____

I feel discouraged in these ways, if any: _____

_____

_____

_____

Insights since treatment: _____

_____

_____

_____

MOVING FORWARD

Ideas to review with counselor or guide: _____

_____

_____

_____

_____

_____

_____

_____

_____

NEW OR UPDATED OUTLETS

Hobbies: _____

_____

_____

Spiritual: _____

_____

_____

Creative: _____

_____

_____

Health and wellness: _____

_____

_____

HOW I FEEL ABOUT WHAT'S HAPPENING

At home: _____

_____

_____

_____

At work: _____

_____

_____

_____

With family: _____

_____

_____

_____

With friends: _____

_____

_____

_____

Personal goals: _____

_____

_____

_____

_____

_____

_____

_____

_____

Any Time Lines

Today's Date: _____

_____

_____

_____

_____

_____

_____

_____

_____

_____

_____

_____

_____

_____

_____

_____

_____

_____

_____

_____

_____

_____

_____

_____

_____

_____

Connection Pages

Today's Date: _____

CURRENT OR RECENT STATUS

Energy Level: 1 2 3 4 5 6 7 8 9 10

Focus Level: 1 2 3 4 5 6 7 8 9 10

Overall Outlook: 1 2 3 4 5 6 7 8 9 10

LOOKING BACK

When I read my notes from the treatment session, I feel: _____

_____

_____

_____

I notice these improvements, if any: _____

_____

_____

_____

I feel discouraged in these ways, if any: _____

_____

_____

_____

Insights since treatment: _____

_____

_____

_____

MOVING FORWARD

Ideas to review with counselor or guide: _____

_____

_____

_____

_____

_____

_____

_____

_____

_____

NEW OR UPDATED OUTLETS

Hobbies: _____

_____

_____

Spiritual: _____

_____

_____

Creative: _____

_____

_____

Health and wellness: _____

_____

_____

_____

HOW I FEEL ABOUT WHAT'S HAPPENING

At home: _____

_____

_____

_____

At work: _____

_____

_____

_____

With family: _____

_____

_____

_____

With friends: _____

_____

_____

_____

Personal goals: _____

_____

_____

_____

_____

_____

_____

_____

_____

_____

_____

Any Time Lines

Today's Date: _____

Acknowledgments

To my husband, Rich Santoro, for endlessly supporting me and celebrating this process. Thank you for believing in me and then, believing with me.

To my parents, Jo Anne Davis and James Glynn Davis, for bringing me into faith so young that even when I got lost, I could find this foundation again and again. I know you both remain with me.

To my thesis committee at East Stroudsburg University, Dr. Holly Wells, Dr. Jasmine Villa, and Professor Bill Broun, for strengthening my research and encouraging me to push my academic work to a meaningful place.

To patients arrived at this page. I applaud your courage and hold open a window of hope for you.

About the Author

Katherine Inez Davis followed a lifelong belief in the power of words to achieve undergraduate and graduate degrees in English and Professional Writing. Her published work earned a Fellowship from the Knight Foundation and awards from the International Association of Business Communicators and Pennsylvania Press Association. She has placed creative writing in Steam Ticket, The Ravens Perch, Green Silk Journal, and Line Zero. Originally from New Jersey, Davis now resides in northeast Pennsylvania.

Made in the USA
Middletown, DE
01 November 2023

41669998R00062